THE OWNER-BUILT FIREPLACE

THE
OWNER-
BUILT
FIREPLACE

ZACK GOULD

Illustrations by James Jones

 VAN NOSTRAND REINHOLD COMPANY
New York Cincinnati Toronto London Melbourne

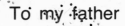

To my father

Acknowledgments
Special thanks to Carol Franco for her patience and enthusiasm draft after draft.

Copyright © 1978 by Litton Educational Publishing, Inc.
Library of Congress Catalog Card Number 78-699
ISBN 0-442-22794-9

Printed in the United States of America
Designed by Loudan Enterprises

Published in 1978 by Van Nostrand Reinhold Company
A division of Litton Educational Publishing, Inc.
135 West 50th Street, New York, NY 10020, U.S.A.

Van Nostrand Reinhold Limited
1410 Birchmount Road
Scarborough, Ontario M1P 2E7, Canada

Van Nostrand Reinhold Australia Pty. Ltd.
17 Queen Street
Mitcham, Victoria 3132, Australia

Van Nostrand Reinhold Company Limited
Molly Millars Lane
Wokingham, Berkshire, England

16 15 14 13 12 11 10 9 8 7 6 5 4 3 2 1

Library of Congress Cataloging in Publication Data

Gould, Zack.
  The owner-built fireplace.

  Bibliography: p.
  Includes index.
  1. Fireplaces—Design and construction.
TH72425.G68   697'.1   78-699
ISBN 0-442-22794-9

CONTENTS

FOREWORD

In the fall of 1972 Zack Gould came into our lives to build our fireplace. In discussing it, and before agreeing to do it, he insisted it be a Rumford design since this was the type of fireplace he believed in both functionally and aesthetically. We hadn't the vaguest idea what a Rumford fireplace was, never having heard of the Count or his inventions, but Zack wasn't interested in doing it any other way so we agreed. All we wanted was a place in our living room where we could warm our hands and other parts, and get cozy during the long New York State winters.

The choice of materials for our fireplace was determined by our environment. Woodstock was once the nation's bluestone capitol, and we had an old farm wall running behind our house made entirely of rough slabs of the stuff. For weeks our living room floor was littered with stones of all shapes and sizes while Zack picked just the right ones for his needs. Some became corners, others part of the arch, and still more fit into the massive jigsaw-puzzle design of the face and chimney. It was a work of consummate craftsmanship combined with a nearly meditative approach to the character of the stone, each one becoming an important individual helping to determine the strength and beauty of the whole. The finished work is something we never tire of looking at.

The moment of truth in any fireplace builder's career is when the first fire is lit, for until then he doesn't really know if it will work the way it's supposed to. Of course, all the Rumford specifications were followed carefully, but will the smoke *really* go up the chimney and not come flooding out into the room? Will the draw of air be sufficient to keep the fire going, but not so strong that it burns up the wood too quickly? After all, every fireplace, like anything else, has its own quirks and peculiarities. The whole family stood around with a slight air of tension as Zack built a meticulous tepee of kindling on the white firebricks. After a moment's hesitation and a deep breath, he lit it up. The fire crackled and blazed, and the smoke rose straight and true.

It's been five years now, and we have sat before many hand-and-soul-warming fires. The Count would have been proud of Zack.

Happy Traum
Woodstock, New York

CHAPTER 1:

PLANNING YOUR FIREPLACE

Some Initial Thoughts

My aim in this book is to take you through the steps of building a fireplace based on the principles of Count Rumford. I will instruct you in the use of tools and materials so that you develop the confidence to shake off that old myth about fireplaces being so damned mysterious and are able to enjoy yourself as much as possible in a tough job.

But let me warn you that building a fireplace is a time-consuming and often frustrating experience. Materials are heavy. Much time is spent carrying bricks and mixing mortar and worrying about rain. And mistakes made with masonry are much harder to correct than mistakes made in almost any other material. Your living room is transformed into a disaster area for the duration of the job and, until you see your first fire, there are times when you wonder if it's all worth it.

If it's any consolation, I've been building fireplaces as a living for a long time now and none are without a certain amount of frustration and apprehension. No two are the same and each has its high and low moments. But there is one thing common to them all—the joy of seeing that first fire taking right off, heating up your kneecaps, and putting up smiles all around.

The Rumford Fireplace

While your mind is whirling with ideas for your fireplace, take stock of these few. First, learn about Benjamin Thompson, Count Rumford, a renaissance man of the eighteenth century and a wizard of efficiency who first recognized the principle of radiant heat. Working on the premise that heat moves in a straight line from its source, Rumford designed a firebox that produces the maximum heat for an inefficient medium.

Count Rumford's personal history and scientific achievements have been well documented (consult the Bibliography). I spent a considerable amount of time researching Count Rumford in the Massachusetts Historical Society before I built my first fireplace. If you are able to find his original publications, I recommend strongly that you read them. If you cannot (or even if you can), I urge you to pick up a copy of *The Forgotten Art of Building a Good Fireplace* by Vrest Orton. Mr. Orton has researched Rumford extensively, gathering his principles of design and efficiency into a well-documented, highly readable, and thoroughly enjoyable book.

I have built all my fireplaces according to Rumford's principles and have received nothing but praise for their efficiency and delight at the presence of a lovely and unique fireplace. I will continue to use the same basic design and you would do well to do the same when building your fireplace.

The most recent literature on fireplaces gives Rumford passing acknowledgment but real appreciation of his principles doesn't seem to have affected the building trade significantly. It seems that most builders, architects, and homeowners are skeptical about something they're unfamiliar with.

> A fireplace built to the Count's proportions seems a little shallow to modern eyes, but this is because we have become accustomed to the deep rectilinear grottoes created by architects in their quest for a "focus of interest" along one wall. It is our taste that may be impaired, for in the heat delivered and the disinclination to smoke, the Rumford fireplaces are among the most sophisticated that have ever been built (Frank Rowsome, Jr., *The Bright and Glowing Place* [Brattleboro, Vermont: Stephen Greene Press, 1975], pp. 171−172).

As I said earlier, all my fireplaces have followed the Count's principles and most of my clients become very nervous about halfway up the firebox. They've never seen such a shallow firebox and can't believe it will work. If I had a nickle for every time I said "trust me," I could retire and build a fireplace for myself. If it's at all possible for you to sit before a working Rumford fireplace, do so. You'll discover why I say "trust me."

Although Rumford designed the most efficient and graceful firebox to be found, it is still a firebox and as such is a terribly inefficient apparatus. Please don't think of a fireplace as an important heat source. It is dangerous to overload a firebox; chimney fires occur when the buildup of creosote (soot) is ignited. This usually happens when a fire is burned too hot, too long, into an uncleaned flue. Remember: today's fireplace is more for warming the heart than the home.

Look at all the fireplaces you can. Take a tape measure with you and a pad and pencil. If you have a camera, all the better. But keep this in mind: no matter what your setting or decor, regardless what materials you use, a Rumford firebox is what will make the difference.

Gathering Ideas

One important item to be aware of in your planning is the size and location of the fireplace. If you're building in an existing house, you probably have little choice, but take your time and look around. The first consideration is the traffic flow in your home. Try to locate the fireplace away from interruption. A bright fire will create a special atmosphere, very relaxing and comforting. The last thing you'll want is to be disturbed by opening doors and people passing back and forth in front of the fireplace. Several years ago I spent a few months in a beautiful old house on a secluded island in Maine. The living room was quite large with an attractive fireplace. The only problem was the location of the fireplace. The layout dictated that the traffic flow constantly interrupt the sanctity of the fireplace. This is unfortunate, but happens all too often.

To anticipate and hopefully avert any space problem, you might build a mock-up of the fireplace with lumber, cardboard, or construction paper. Establish an idea of what you'll be faced with. Can you afford the space to keep the entire fireplace inside the exterior walls of the house? Or would it be better to keep the breast of the fireplace flush with the wall and build the bulk of the chimney outside? Set up your model and see what happens to your space when people come and go.

As I mentioned earlier, you may not have much choice. If it seems that there is only one place for the fireplace, be sure to check your plumbing and wiring. Pipes and wires can sometimes be moved but this is usually expensive. If you don't know about such things, find someone who does.

I can't design your fireplace nor can I foresee the particular problems you may have when you finally introduce a fireplace and chimney into your home. The particulars vary, but the principles remain the same.

After much thought I decided that the best approach here would be to build a simple brick fireplace with one extra flue starting in the basement. The process of building is described in such a way that it can be completely done inside the house if you wish, or accomplished with the chimney breast running outside. The main emphasis is on showing you what goes on inside and out of a Rumford fireplace and chimney.

In the following pages I take you through the steps and stages of building a fireplace—from the tools and materials you will need to the tricks and insights necessary to putting together a handsome, well-drawing Rumford fireplace.

CHAPTER 2:

TOOLS

Most of the tools required for building a fireplace are not terribly expensive nor do you need many. Most can be used for projects other than fireplace construction, and you'll be amazed at the number of other uses you'll find for the tools once you know how to use them.

Another point to keep in mind: a good used tool will serve you as well as a good new tool and should be considerably less expensive. Most communities, large and small, have places where you can buy used tools. If not, you would be wise to place an ad in your local paper listing the tools you need. You'll not only come away with a bargain but probably valuable information as well. Most people who know how to use the tools will be more than willing to share their ideas, tips, experience, and insights. Try not to be intimidated if this is the first fireplace you've ever built. Some people have done it; more wish they had.

Good tools are as important as the skill and knowledge in using them. Hence it is important that you have a specific idea of the tools you will need. In no particular order these tools include:

Medium Sized Trowel

Trowels come in many assorted sizes and shapes. I recommend the 9-inch size because it was comfortable for me when I built my first fireplace. Use a larger one if you like, but a smaller one is inadequate for brick, block, and stone.

Levels

Levels come in many different lengths. I recommend high-quality, 4-foot and 2-foot builders' levels and a 10- or 12-inch torpedo level. If you buy wooden levels, be sure the edges are trimmed with metal. When an all-wood level is used with brick, block, and stone, the edges tend to get irregular with use or wear down enough to make the level inaccurate.

Large Mixing Tub

A large mixing tub is needed to mix mortar. You can buy one that is made of steel or vulcanized rubber, but these are quite expensive. This is one item you may never use again. I recommend that you build one of wood. You've probably got lumber of one kind or another lying around (or possibly stacked neatly!). Build a wooden mixing tub 4 feet wide, 6 feet long, with sides and ends made of 2-inch by 10-inch boards and a bottom of ½-inch-or-thicker plywood. (Dimensions may vary if larger but don't go smaller as you need the space.)

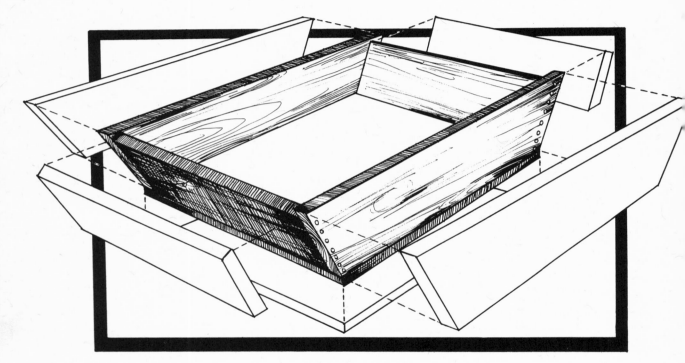

2–1. Build your mortar tub with 2-by-10s.

Small Mortar Tub

You will need a small mortar tub to work out of. It should be small and light enough to follow you around the job easily but sturdy enough to hold four or five shovelfulls of mortar. Again, you can buy these in steel or rubber but you end up with the same re-use problem.

You *could* build one along the same lines as the large tub, substituting lighter materials and smaller dimensions; however, I solved this problem years ago when I bought a baby bathtub in a Goodwill store for $.25. It's lightweight, easy to clean, durable, and very cheap.

Shovel

You will also need a good-quality, long-handled, pointed No. 2 shovel.

Hoe

A hoe is necessary for mixing mortar. Don't use a garden variety hoe; it's much too small. Buy or borrow a large hoe especially made for this purpose. The added expense is worth it. Every batch of mortar that you mix will contain about 350 pounds of sand, mortar, cement, and water. The easier it is to mix, the happier you will be.

Bucket

Any good, heavy-duty bucket is adequate for transporting mortar from mixing tub to working tub. If you're going to buy buckets for this project, I recommend a rubberized type which is easy to clean and fairly impervious to the beating it gets.

Miscellaneous Tools

You should also have on hand the following tools. Their various functions will either be obvious or explained as you need them or both:

framing square
combination square
bevel
tape measure
folding rule
line blocks
string
jointer
brick hammer
3 lb block hammer
brick set
1½-inch cold chisel
plumb bob

While we're discussing tools and before you've begun to use them, let me caution you about an important point: mason's tools, including tubs and buckets, *must* be cleaned thoroughly every day after use. You can be as sloppy as you want during their use but you must wash off all the mortar at the end of the day. If you don't, you'll have to chip it off the next day. This is time-consuming, frustrating, and a very inconsiderate way to treat your tools.

CHAPTER 3

MATERIALS

The spectrum of materials available to you is quite broad. There are hundreds of different kinds of brick to choose from, various types of block, and cut and natural stone. What you use will depend partly on taste and partly on availability.

Think of your materials this way:

1. *The Face.* What you see—block, stone, brick. This includes the foundation face.

2. *The Internal Flue System.* What you don't see—flue tile, brick, cement block—going on behind the face.

3. *Mortar.* The bonding agent. Basically mortar is a combination of sand, Portland cement, and lime or masonry cement. The various ways to mix mortar are discussed later; for now, you only need to consider the ingredients for mixing mortar in planning for materials.

The Face

If you haven't already decided what to use for face material, take a look around. You will probably decide on one of three materials—block, stone, or brick.

Block

Don't discount concrete block as a material for a handsome fireplace. Its surface can be used as a base for stucco, plaster, and wood. It is relatively easy to use, and cheap and fast to construct. If you use block for any wall of your chimney, be sure to check your local building codes. Generally, codes call for a thicker wall where block is used.

Stone

Stone is certainly the most interesting material you could use. Man's oldest and strongest building medium is still abundant and still handsome.

Working with stone requires a different approach from that used with any other material. It's somewhat like working with a jigsaw puzzle, but unlike the puzzle whose pieces all fit by design, laying up stone becomes more difficult as you use up your stone supply and when tying sections together or nearing completion.

If you use stone as a face material, keep in mind these considerations. Be sure you have enough stock on the job or available from the same source. Also, be sure it is all the same kind of stone, that is, all weathered fieldstone, all quarry rubble, all cut and dressed, and so forth. If you run out of the kind of stone you started with and have to finish with another, you'll have an awkward-looking chimney.

It shouldn't take long to discover the kind of local stone available. I say local because the further away you get from the source of the stone, the more it will cost to transport. Fieldstone is lovely and a favorite of most people, myself included. It is usually found in stone fences, which are fast becoming an endangered species. You may have difficulty finding fieldstone or it may be very expensive or both.

If you live anywhere near a stone quarry, it may be possible to get your hands on enough "quarry rubble." Quarry rubble is a term used for the pieces of stone remaining after a larger stone has been "dressed," or cut to its finished specifications. Quarry rubble is generally not weathered very much but usually has enough interesting properties to make it worth investigating.

If your house is newly built, there may be a good quantity of

fresh, or green, stone left over from excavation. My personal feeling is to avoid these. They're often not attractive, tend to be covered with gouges from back hoes and bulldozers, and require extensive scrubbing and cleaning.

Streams, riverbeds, and beaches provide excellent stock for stonework, but check with your local environmental board, conservation office, or Army Corps of Engineers. In many coastal areas it is illegal to add to or subtract from any shoreline without the permission of the Army Corps of Engineers. Every stone taken from the beach has its effect on the overall posture of the tide flow. These basic principles hold true of streams and rivers as well.

Brick

Of all the materials available to you, brick is certainly the most common. There are hundreds of different kinds of brick, both new and used. As with stone, a little investigating will tell you what is available.

With brick, as with stone, it is extremely important that you get all your materials from the same source. You'll have no problem with new brick, but be careful about used brick. A single brick house probably used two or more types of brick in its construction and you may not want to mix them. The face brick used for the outside walls is denser, and often a little smaller than the brick used for the common inside walls. So even if your brick comes from the same house, be careful. Used, old, common bricks vary in size slightly from brick to brick but if they are all from the same lot your overall face will be consistent.

Before you take any used bricks for free, or interest yourself in a pile of uncleaned bricks, be *very* careful to check the consistency of the mortar still left on the bricks. Most old lime mortar cleans off easily by hitting it with your brick hammer. However, some later types of cement or cement-lime mortars can be extremely difficult to clean and absolutely not worth your while.

Every pile of old bricks seems to have a few "softies" in it. These bricks are softer than the rest, more porous, and lighter in weight. They tend to crumble around the edges and for some reason have an obvious orange cast. Softies are to be expected, but if you discover more than, say, one in twenty, you might want to reconsider. I do not advise using softies. Their structural properties are not very good and they will continue to crumble, depositing unwanted dust and chips on your mantel or floor.

Old, common brick may have to be soaked before being set in mortar. Often they are so dry that they will suck the water out of a wet bed of mortar before it has a chance to temper. At some point during the construction of the foundation, set a couple of bricks together with mortar and see what happens. The mortar should remain reasonably plastic for a couple of hours. If it dries out too quickly, you should hose down the pile several times a day for a few days before you start to use the bricks. You may have to continue the wetting process all along, depending on how dry or porous the bricks are. Don't get them *too* wet or you'll create a mess when you lay the brick; the mortar you lay it on will ooze out and run on the bricks below. Experiment with your pile of bricks until you know how much water they need. Try to arrange things in such a way that you'll always have a day's worth of bricks dampened ahead of you. Once you get moving nicely with your work, it's exasperating to have to drop everything and start soaking bricks.

As far as cleaning used bricks, remember that only one side of a possible six shows (one long side and one short side for corner bricks). You should not get terribly involved in scrubbing the bricks with wire brushes and muriatic acid. As long as enough of the old mortar is removed so as not to interfere with the actual laying of brick, you'll be fine. Small nubs, or a slight layer of old mortar, will not hinder you. Use your judgment.

Internal Flue System

The internal flue system consists of a separate flue tile for each thing—fireplace, wood stove, furnace, etc.—to be vented, and each of these tiles must be separated from the other by at least 4 inches of solid masonry. There are also a few places that need to be filled. As you will see in later chapters, there's quite a bit going on behind the face. We'll take a closer look as we build our way up.

Mortar

Mortar, in one form or another, has been around since mud. The functions of mortar are fairly obvious: (1) It is a bonding agent for masonry units (not a glue). (2) It presents a water and weather resistant barrier. (3) It provides a uniform appearance.

The Egyptians and Romans mixed a volcanic ash with lime and water for their mortar. Nineteenth- and twentieth-century technology has given us a superior and highly durable quality Portland cement and masonry cement.

Portland cement is not a brand name. It is a type of cement developed in England in 1824, which, when hardened, looked like a stone found on the Isle of Portland. Its development has gone through some changes and refinements since then, but basically it is a combination of quarried limestone, oyster shells, clay, iron ore, silica sand, and blast furnace slag. Masonry cement contains

Portland cement, but it also contains ground limestone and gypsum. For more information on these cements, I suggest you write to the companies that produce masonry cement and Portland cement. You can get their names and addresses from local building supply companies.

Sand

Sand is the essential bonding agent in any mortar or cement. You'll probably use about four tons of it in your fireplace! Sand is easy to obtain anywhere and there are only a few things to keep in mind. First, be sure to use pit sand. Each little grain has sharp edges, good for bonding. Beach sand has individual, rounded grains; hence it is poor for bonding. In addition, beach sand is full of salt which does not combine well with lime and cement. Stream and river sand likewise has grains which are too smooth for the kind of bonding needed in fireplace construction.

You can generally buy pit sand, delivered, by the yard. A cubic yard, 27 cubic feet, equals about 2700 lbs depending on how much rain you've had recently. Also, you can usually order the sand "screened" or sifted so that there are no particles larger than ⅛ inch. This is sometimes called "brick sand" or "mortar sand." The cost is greater if you order sand this way but it eliminates doing the screening yourself.

Should you choose to screen the sand yourself, build a frame made of 2-by-4s, 6 feet tall and 4 feet wide. Stretch ⅛-inch galvanized wire mesh over the perimeter of this frame and staple or nail it securely. Stand the frame on the ground at about 20 to 30 degrees from the perpendicular with the wire facing you. Support one end with two 2-by-4 legs attached to the frame. Toss shovelfulls of sand to the top of the frame; as the sand rolls down the screen the small particles pass through the screen and the large ones remain on the face side of the screen. Screening sand this way is actually a very enjoyable pastime as well as constructive labor for well-meaning neighbors and noisy children.

With three or four yards of sand sitting in your driveway or backyard, you're bound to have the most popular dog and cat privy for miles. It's better to discover that before it ends up in your mixing tub. (Believe me, it happens.) If you anticipate crowds of animals and children gathering to pay homage to your sand pile, you may want to construct a three-sided bin to contain the spillage. I once walked out of a house to find my newly delivered pile of sand infested with seven small children, five large dogs, and several mothers trying unsuccessfully to break up the party. It was all great fun but I lost about one-half yard of sand to pockets, cuffs, ears, and general disbursement. (Kids love to throw sand!)

Mixing Mortar

Mixing a batch of mortar is like mixing a batch of dough for your favorite bread. You have a list of ingredients; they simply need to be combined properly.

Color of mortar may be an important factor in the mix. Keep in mind that you can produce virtually any shade between black and white, and almost any other color in the rainbow. Portland and masonry cements come in shades from white to very dark, and additives are available to produce other color variations. Experiment with mixes until you get what you want. Then be sure to keep your mixes consistent and stick with the same brand-name materials; otherwise, the results will vary.

There are various combinations of ingredients which can be combined to produce a good brick mortar. It's rare to find any two masons who use the same proportions for mixing mortar. The proportions I suggest here are those I learned from an extremely competent "old timer." Subsequently, in researching technical manuals, I've learned that this mix is recommended for extremely heavy loads, violent winds, earthquakes, or severe frost action! Choose what you're comfortable with. For purposes of technique, here's how I mix a batch: Into your reasonably level mortar tub throw twenty No. 2 shovelfulls of sand, each shovelfull weighing about 10 lbs. Add one-half bag of mortar cement and one-half bag of Portland cement. Make a reasonable guesstimate. With your hoe mix everything together dry. Pull back and forth a couple of times, or more if necessary, until it seems to be mixed well. Pull the dry mixture to one end of the tub and prepare to add water. How much water you should add depends upon the wetness of the sand. Start off by dumping in a full bucket of water. Pull the dry mixture to the water with smooth, controlled strokes of the hoe. As the mixture thickens, the movement is a back and forth motion of the hoe of no more than 12 inches. Avoid any long strokes of the hoe as they won't really help the mixing action. Add more water as needed, pulling dry to wet.

At some point, about midway or so through this process, you may want to stop pulling in the dry mixture and concentrate on getting what you have to its proper consistency. (Unless you're working terribly fast, there's no sense in mixing it all at once anyway.) You will have reached the proper consistency when you can pick up a trowelfull of mortar, hold it vertically, and have the mortar fall off cleanly after only a slight pause. If the mortar does not stay for that brief pause, and it doesn't seem to be too wet, your mixture is probably not rich enough; that is, you may have too much sand in the mix. If, when the mortar falls off the trowel, it leaves a lot of itself on the trowel and in general seems sticky and hard to move around, you probably don't have enough sand in the mix. If you're in trouble like this, add more of the lacking ingredient until you get it just right. This is a terrible way to spend your time so get used to mixing it properly the first time around.

Once you've mixed a batch, don't worry about it too much. You may want to cover it if the sun is very hot or if it's raining; but you can pretty much leave it alone for awhile. If work is not progressing very quickly, check the mortar occasionally. Add water and retemper if it starts to set up on you.

Gathering and understanding materials takes some time. Be patient, ask questions, touch, and observe.

CHAPTER 4:

BUILDING THE FOUNDATION

Before we begin building the foundation, let me point out that it is unlikely that your particular situation will match what you are shown here. I'll be showing you how to build a complete four-sided foundation. You may only need to build three sides using the house foundation as the fourth. This is fine. My real purpose is to show you how to work with the tools and materials and to furnish an overall design and method. As long as you know the basics and are not afraid to use a tape measure, you'll be able to deal with any situation that arises.

Footing

The footing is the first thing you'll construct in building your fireplace. The footing is a slab of concrete below frost line, reinforced with steel rod upon which the foundation of your fireplace is built. The size and shape of your fireplace determines the size of the footing. The *entire* weight of your chimney rests on this. Don't cut any corners.

Since it is extremely important that the footing be done properly, I suggest you do a little extra homework. Follow my directions carefully but consult local building codes as well as local contractors and masons. Individual areas of the country have different frost lines, drainage patterns, and soil properties. I bow gracefully to any local advice you get from competent people.

4–1. Place your footing below frost line. Tie reinforcing rod with wire at every intersection. The bottom of your footing should be level and solid. Remove form after twenty-four hours.

The footing should be 8 inches wider on every side than the dimensions of the chimney breast. The top of the footing should come to the same level as the footing for the house. The footing should be 12 inches thick, with ¾-inch reinforcing rod, wired together in a grid of 8-inch squares. The steel grid should be in the middle of the concrete so lift it off the ground with bricks. A good footing mix is 1 part Portland cement, 2½ parts sand, and 3 parts gravel (¾-inch aggregate).

When you're digging the hole for the footing, remember that you'll be working there. Allow at least 2 feet extra all around to fit you and your blocks and tools. If you're coming up on the inside of the house, you will have to break through the basement floor and follow the same directions. If you have a concrete and wire floor in your basement you will have a terrible job ahead of you.

Be sure the dirt bottom as well as the top of the footing is level. Probably the easiest way to level the top is to build a wooden form for the concrete, making the top level all around. Then just scrape the top with a reasonably straight piece of wood. (See Figure 4-1)

At this point it is important to remember to set the top of the footing at an even increment of your foundation material, *down from* the point at which you'll pour the hearth slab. You may want to make your footing a few inches thicker, but under no circumstances make it thinner. If you find that the top of the footing needs to be lower, dig your hole deeper and maintain the proper thickness by dropping the whole unit. In fact, the deeper you go with your footing the better off you will be.

Block Foundation

Cement blocks are not as exciting or aesthetically pleasing as the brick or stone you will be using later, but they are practical, strong, and lay up faster. Use 8-inch block with three holes. In your area you may only be able to get block with two holes. Don't worry. If (as in the example here) you find a need for 8-inch-long sections, it is usually possible to purchase 8-inch *half* blocks. If you would rather have a brick face in your basement, use the same overall dimensions I give but use 4-inch block where I call for 8-inch and make up the outside 4 inches with brick. (See Figure 4-2)

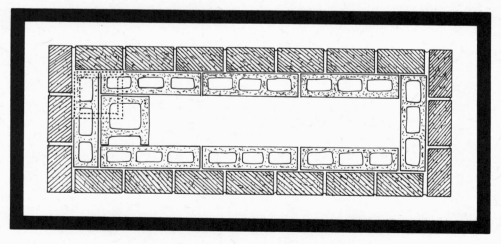

4–2. Four-inch block with brick face.

Assuming your footing is level, start by dropping four plumb lines from the four corners of the projected, finished chimney breast as it will be on the first floor. Scratch your outline on the concrete surface and prepare to set your leads, that is, those blocks or bricks that are set first on each corner of the face. (See Figure 4-3)

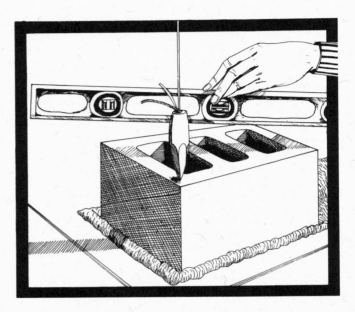

4-3. Each lead block will be set with the corner to the plumb line, level from right to left, front to back.

Lay out a three-sided rectangular bed of mortar corresponding to the underside of a corner block. Mortar is laid only under the edges of the blocks, not under the partitions. Until you really get the feel of your trowel, the laying of mortar will be an awkward process. Take your time; relax. Don't get in the habit of using your hands to work with the mortar. Between the abrasive action of the sand and the burning qualities of the lime, you'll end up with red, cracked, and sore fingers. You'll probably do it anyway. You'll see a whole trowelful of mortar sliding off the block and you'll want to catch it. Until you know how to use the trowel, it is tempting to use your bare hands to help. This may be the only time you'll work with mortar so you may never get the trowel action just right, but relax and do your best.

The bed of mortar should be about 1 inch thick. The weight of the block, plus the pressure you exert in setting it, will squish the mortar down to between ½ to ⅜ inches thick. Measure down from the point at which your *last* course of blocks will be laid (the last course ends where the hearth slab is to be poured). Be sure your lead block corresponds to your layout. If it does, you'll have smooth sailing all the way up with ⅜-inch joints. If not, you'll find out the hard way that an inch or so can be a real problem to correct.

Laying Block

Holding the block with both hands, tapered flange up, set the block to the plumb line and mortar bed in as level and plumb a fashion as possible. Do not slide the block in the mortar; keep it as straight vertically as possible. Remember the block has to be level from end to end and from back to front, and the corner must be exactly where it should be. Don't be discouraged; it can be tricky. Above all, don't be lax. If you don't get your leads right you'll have a real mess before long.

Repeat this process with a corner block for each corner. Make sure that all corner blocks are themselves level and level with each other. Before you're through, you'll be setting up two or three lead courses at a time; but for now I would suggest that you complete your entire first course. (See Figure 4-4)

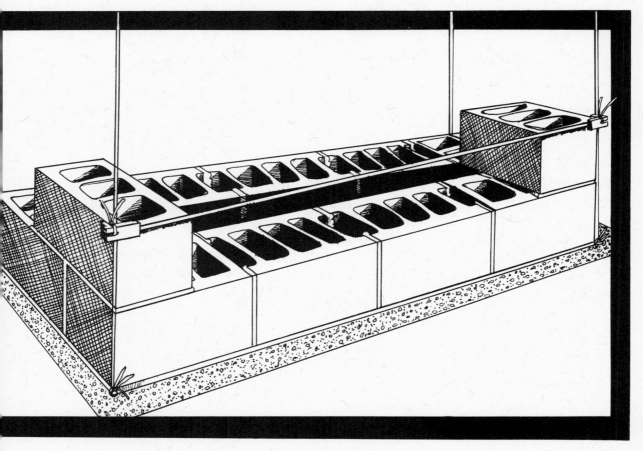

4–4. First course complete with leads set for second course.

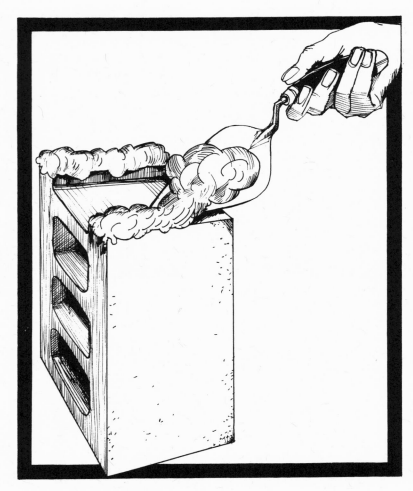

4–5. Lay mortar on "ears."

Using two line blocks, stretch a line between any two corners. The string will go from the top of one corner to the top of the other, stretched tight enough so that the line doesn't sag. When you lay the filler blocks for this course, you will first "butter" the joining edges of the block to be laid. These buttered joints have a fairly regular tendency to drop off when you don't want them to. (See Figures 4-5, 4-6, and 4-7) Be sure your mortar is not too sandy. Keep at it; this process takes much less time than stuffing the joints with mortar after the block is set.

Grasp the block with two hands, lift it over the string, and gently, firmly, and *plumbly* set it onto the waiting bed of mortar using the string as a guide for the top front edge of the block. The block should be as close to the string as possible without actually touching it. Be sure the string and block are not touching. If they are, the string will be off and the next block will be further out and so on. Every time you lay a new block, the mortar joint you've created vertically between blocks will inevitably push the string out of whack. Strike the joint before final positioning of the block, as shown in Figure 4-8.

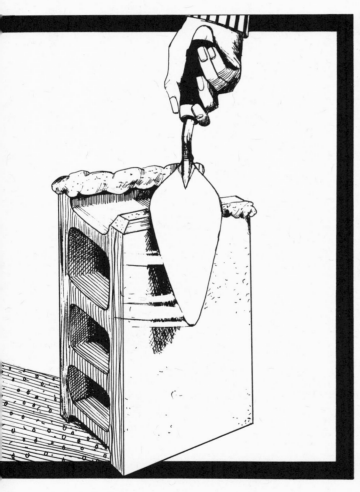

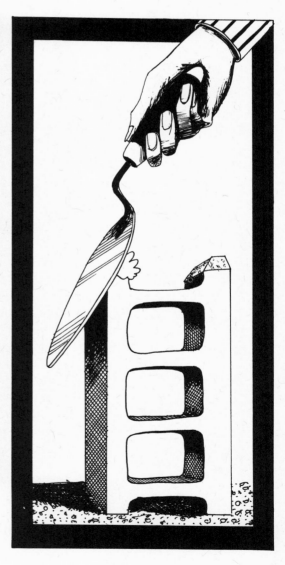

4–6, 4–7. Striking motion will compress mortar.

4–8. Striking a mortar joint.

Sometimes you'll find that you've lined up the string and the block perfectly but that you're out of level from front to back. Or perhaps you're out of level the long way, or you're level but the whole block is too high. Maneuvering a block when it's sitting in a bed of mortar is difficult until you get a feel for it. If you're below the line, forget it. Remove the block, add more mortar, and try again. If one end is level or slightly above and the other end has to come down more, hold the lowest end firmly with one hand in such a way that it won't move—up, down, or sideways. While the lower, or level end is under control, tape the other end into approximate position. (See Figures 4-9—4-12) I say approximate because you'll have to reverse the process and go back and forth as many times as necessary to get the block level. Use the same process for the front-to-back level, making sure to hold and tap only in the very middle of each edge. This sounds terribly complicated and time-consuming but in fact takes only seconds once you're used to it.

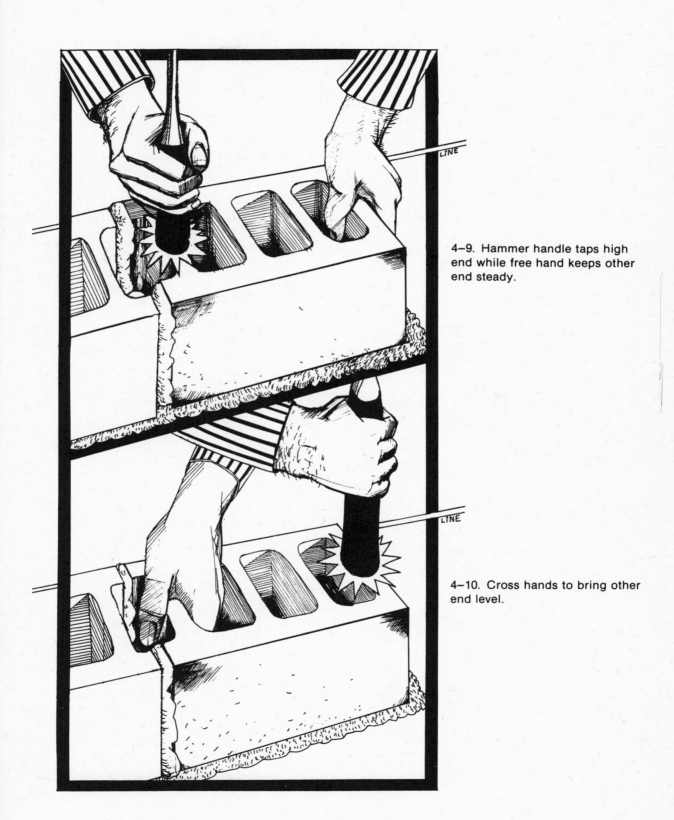

4–9. Hammer handle taps high end while free hand keeps other end steady.

4–10. Cross hands to bring other end level.

33

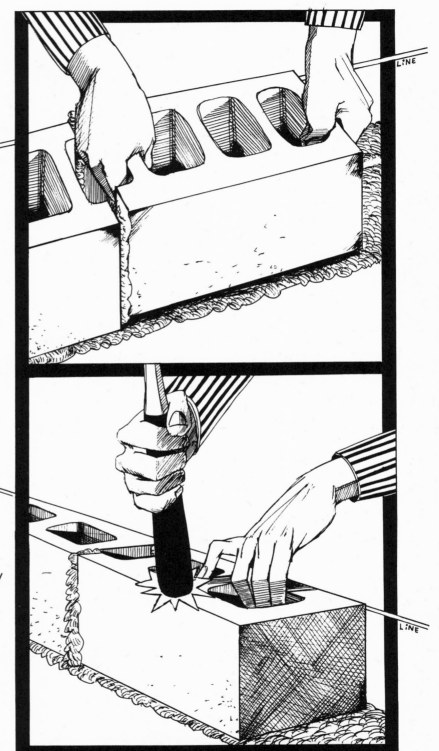

4–11. Set block gently, firmly, and plumbly.

4–12. Hold front of block steady while tapping back.

Get comfortable with this leveling process early because you'll be using the same principle for both blocks and bricks throughout construction. There's nothing worse than going through the entire process of laying mortar, buttering joints, and lifting the block over the string (especially when it reaches eye level) only to find you've goofed again. Try to make all your mistakes early, around knee level, when the block is much easier to maneuver.

After you get up a couple of courses, it may seem like you've been wasting a lot of mortar. As you set a block in place, the excess mortar will plop to your toes or to the ground between the walls. Don't worry about this as it is normal and there's not much you can do about it. Much can be saved by striking the joints and flipping the excess mortar back into the tub.

Tooling Joints

As you bring up the block work, you should check the mortar in the joints every so often. Before the mortar sets up too much, you will want to "tool" the joints. After the excess mortar has been struck from three or four courses of block, take your jointer, or jointing tool, and run it along the joints, horizontally and vertically. Press firmly and go over the joints until you produce a smooth surface as illustrated in Figures 4-13 and 4-14. The action of the jointer compresses and smooths the mortar, bringing water to the surface. The resulting joint will be more weather- and watertight than a struck joint.

4–13, 4–14. Tooling the joints. This is a good time to fill any gaps.

Cutting Flue Tiles

Use an 8-inch-by-8-inch-tile flue liner which is standard for venting furnaces or wood stoves. (However, check your local building codes.) We will be creating here a separate chimney inside the fireplace foundation which will continue throughout the entire chimney breast. There will be unseen places where it will not much resemble a chimney; those will be examined later.

You are now about to cut your first flue tile. There are two ways to do it, neither of which is fun. The bigger the flue, the less enjoyable it will be and the more expensive if it breaks. The first procedure is as follows:

1. Mark the flue tile for a 45-degree cut at the proper length. The four corners of this tile are rounded, so take your time and get one good line drawn all the way around. A combination square and/or bevel are very helpful.

2. Fill the flue tile with sand. Hopefully the sand will absorb enough of the shock from the hammer and chisel to keep it from cracking. This does not always happen; cross your fingers.

3. Take out a 1½-inch cold chisel. Flue tiles are notoriously irregular and I find a wider chisel can't cope with dips and moguls as well as a smaller one.

4. Holding the chisel perpendicular to your tile, start striking the chisel as you move it along the line, one strike per chisel length. Try to get into a fairly steady rhythm of striking and moving. Strike, move, strike, move. (See Figure 4-15) You won't see much of a result the first time around. Keep steady and regular with good solid strikes with the hammer. On the second pass, stay exactly with the line but try to hit places you passed over on the first pass. Keep steady. The chisel is setting up a pattern of shock waves that will eventually work themselves through the tile.

Sometimes this process takes as little as two or three passes around the tile, resulting in a perfectly clean cut. It can just as easily be ruined by splitting down the middle after the first pass or take you ten passes and split the wrong way on your last hammer strike.

The other method to cut a flue tile is to use a masonry blade in an electric circular saw. Set the depth of the blade just enough to go through the tile. Wear goggles and a breathing mask and move the saw very slowly. Be sure to work outdoors when you use this process; the saw creates a great amount of dust. This will result in a very smooth, even cut on your tile and raise hell with your saw. Either way, your end result will be two pieces of flue tile with 45-degree cuts.

Before you set the flue tile, it is important to know that your block-laying expertise will have to include the fact that you are now incorporating a flue system as part of your fireplace foundation. In essence, you will be building a separate chimney but still keeping it a structural part of the foundation as a whole. This is where the 4-inch blocks come into play. This is where you learn to cut blocks. And this is where I try to keep you from going crazy.

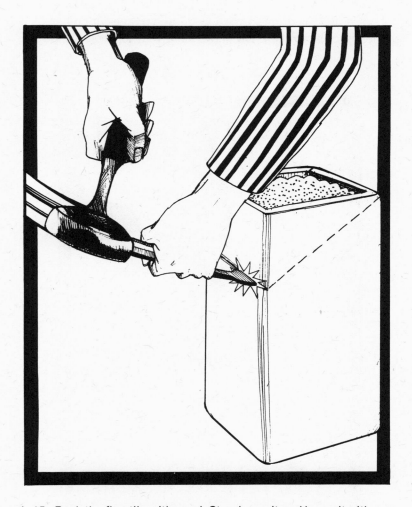

4-15. Pack the flue tile with sand. Stand over it and brace it with your knees.

Cutting Block

The materials you're likely to use in cutting and shaping block are 8-inch block, 4-inch block, and concrete brick. Be sure you order and use only the high-quality, concrete type of block and brick. There are lightweight, porous materials of the same size, sometimes called cinder block; don't be confused. Be sure to explain to the people at the mason yard what you'll be using them for.

An 8-inch block is, in fact, 7⅝ inches by 7⅝ inches by 15⅝ inches. Generally, with 4-inch block, the holes are exposed on the bottom and sealed off on the top by a thin layer of cement. For purposes of illustration, we show them with top holes exposed.

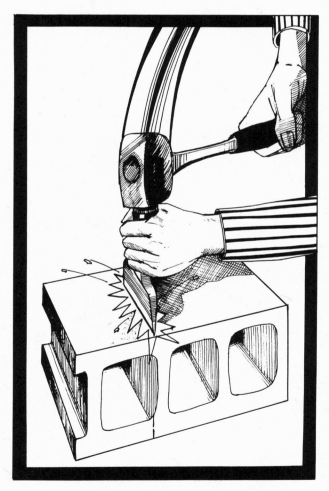

4–16. Strike chisel firmly, but not extra hard.

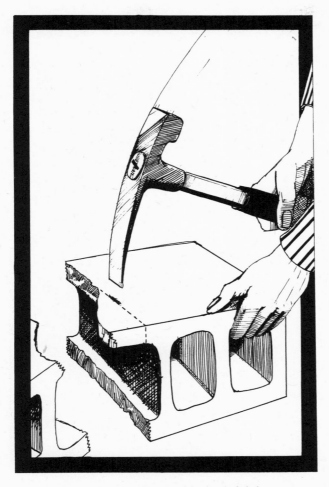

4–17. Trim ragged edges with the brick hammer.

To cut your block, lay it on a resilient surface—preferably sand (to keep dirt or mud from sticking to the block). At the length desired, scribe a line around the block. Using a 4-inch brick set and a 3 lb hammer, strike the block at the line all around, turning the block as you work. If the block doesn't split the first time around try again, perhaps hitting a little harder. (See Figures 4-16 and 4-17)

Don't get frustrated; this process may take some practice. Find some blocks that were damaged in transit and practice on them. You will probably end up with some jagged edges; just be sure that no part of the edge extends past your required measurement. It will be harder to butter the cut edges than the edges of uncut factory blocks, but it is possible. So, after the block is cut, lay it up the same as you would any other block.

A 4-inch block is cut the same way. Concrete bricks can also be cut this way, or can be cut to "bats" by holding them in your palm and striking them in the middle with a brick hammer. (See Figures 4-18 and 4-19)

4–18. A 4-inch block will cut with less strain than an 8-inch block.

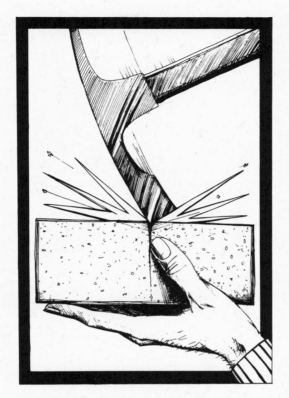

4–19. Cut concrete brick approximately in half for "bats."

Starting Basement Flue

You can start your basement flue at any height you wish depending on its use. (If it's to vent a wood stove or fireplace on the second floor, start it above the second floor.) If you don't know right away what you'll be using it for, start it high, say 6 feet, or your ninth course off the floor. Better to vent up than down.

Bring your block work level all around at the course that is about 6 feet from the finished basement floor. To start the flue system join two flue tiles, each with a 45-degree miter. The vertical flue tile is set 4 inches in from each edge and continues in this position until the chimney is finished. The horizontal flue tile serves as a connecting link from the furnace or stove (or whatever it is venting) to the start of the vertical flue tile. (See Figure 4-20)

Before you set your flue tiles you should start the outside leads which will now be 4-inch block. The first block you set runs from left to right (as you face it from the basement). Treat this the same way you have treated all your other leads. The only difference is the width. Next to this, running the length of the wall, set a full-length, 8-inch block.

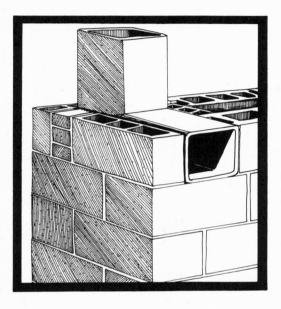

4-20

4-20. Flue tiles relative to each other and block foundation.

The next block you set runs from the inside left corner toward the outside. You now have two leads set for the next course but you will also notice a 4-inch gap between the two blocks. This happened because you switched from 8-inch blocks; hence you lost 4 inches. Don't worry. Fill this gap with three concrete brick bats. (See Figure 4-21) Now go back to the outside left corner and set another 4-inch lead with the length running toward you to the basement. Set one more 4-inch block from left to right on the same outside course. Here you've started the actual chimney for the basement flue; the outside walls of the chimney will hold the flue tile in place while you set it. (See Figure 4-22)

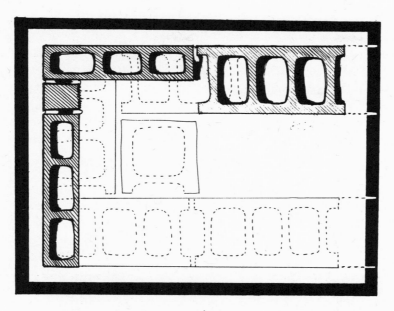

4–21. Begin use of 4-inch block to make room for flue tile. Note 4-inch bats.

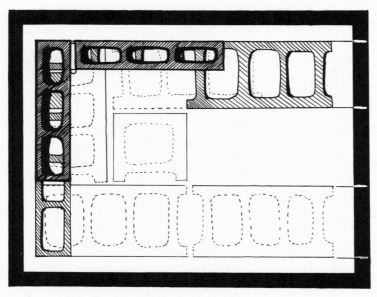

4–22. Use 4-inch block for second course. Note 4-inch block overlapping 8-inch block.

At this point set the horizontal flue tile in place. Don't set it in a bed of mortar. You may find the outside height of the tile greater than 8 inches, and the mortar will exaggerate the adjustment to the next course of block. However, *do* mortar the sides. Next, butter the cut edge of the tile and set the vertical tile in place. If you've cut your tile with a chisel, the edges may be a little ragged. Don't worry; just make sure the mortar seals off any cracks. Be sure to strike off any mortar protruding on the inside of the flue tile.

Check the vertical tile for plumb. At this point, with both tiles set, you will begin the inside wall of the chimney. Cut a 4-inch block to a length of 12 inches and mortar it next to the flue tile, between the foundation walls.

Now come back to the inside foundation wall and cut an 8-inch block to a length of 12 inches. Mortar this block so that the right-hand side of it lines up with the middle of the block beneath it. (See Figure 4-23) The gap left between the block and the flue tile should be filled with mortar. A full-size, 8-inch block serves as the lead for the source that bridges the horizontal tile. If the flue tile is higher than 8 inches, you will need to cut the bottom of this block enough for it to set to the line.

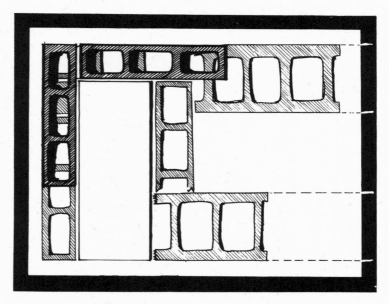

4–23. Horizontal flue tile is set; inner chimney begins.

By the time you're this far along with the foundation, you should consider what material you'll be using for the hearth. Go ahead with your reading and start to figure your measurements. The distance between the block and the flooring is important if you plan to keep your hearth at floor level. Add the thickness of the hearth material (which can be any noncombustible material) plus ½ inch for a mortar bed and 3 inches for a subhearth slab. (More than 3 inches is fine if it helps you work out your courses properly.) Bring the block work up to within this measurement and you'll be prepared for the subhearth.

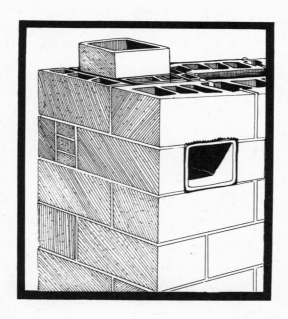

CHAPTER 5:

HEARTH, FIREBOX, AND ARCH

The floor area cut out to accommodate the block foundation and the extension for the hearth will vary with every house. The example presented here is typical and I'm sure you'll be able to figure your way around any particular variation you may have.

The Hearth

Figure 5-1 shows our "typical" block foundation with a "typical" framing detail of the floor. When you get this close to the floor, you will need to think about preparing the hearth. A standard hearth runs the width of the chimney breast and protrudes 16 inches into the room. The main function of the hearth is to offer protection against flying sparks and rolling logs. Most local codes won't allow anything less than 16 inches beyond the fireplace—be sure to check.

Brace the joists properly with lumber before you begin to cut away the floor and subfloor, exposing the joists. The joists will have to be undercut to allow for a double header. After your headers are installed, you can remove the bracing.

The next step is to pour a subhearth in such a way that the finished hearth works out to be level with the finished floor. Most published instructions on this subject fail to take into account the fact that your house could be different from their drawing. Don't hesitate to adjust your block work or brick to fit your particular need.

Figures 5-1 and 5-2 show the block and flue liner with the framing headed off for the hearth. In Figures 5-3 and 5-4, the brick work is started for the finished breast.

Before the subhearth is poured, you need some preparation. Fill the holes of the top course of blocks with rubble tightly enough so the concrete will not seep all the way to the basement. Next, cover the hole between the blocks with a noncombustible material (sheet asbestos, tin, steel, etc.). Put down a piece just large enough to cover the hole (Figure 5-2).

Place a piece of plywood between the block and the header in such a way that it can be removed. Keep in mind that you should have *at least* a 2- to 3-inch-thick hearth slab with a ½-inch reinforcing rod. Hence, measure down from your finished floor to be sure you have enough room for your hearth material.

When the concrete is poured for the subhearth, it will be contained on the back and sides by a first course of brick, and in front by the header. The first course of bricks should be laid at least the day before you pour concrete. Even a small amount of concrete has quite a force behind it and could easily push aside one or two courses of bricks before they're set. Don't worry about the appearance of these first brick courses, they will not be visible.

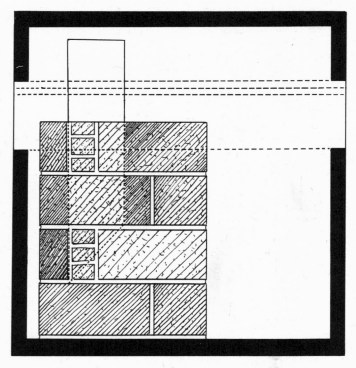

5-1. Block foundation with framing indicated by dotted lines.

After the first course of brick is set and the holes are filled or covered, lay in a grid of ½-inch reinforcing rod, 3 or 4 inches on centers, elevated with scraps of brick or block so that it will be in the center of the pour. Mix and pour the subhearth the same way you did the footing and bring it level all around.

Now relax and let the concrete cure overnight. If you finish this process early in the day, give yourself a small vacation; you have a lot more work to do.

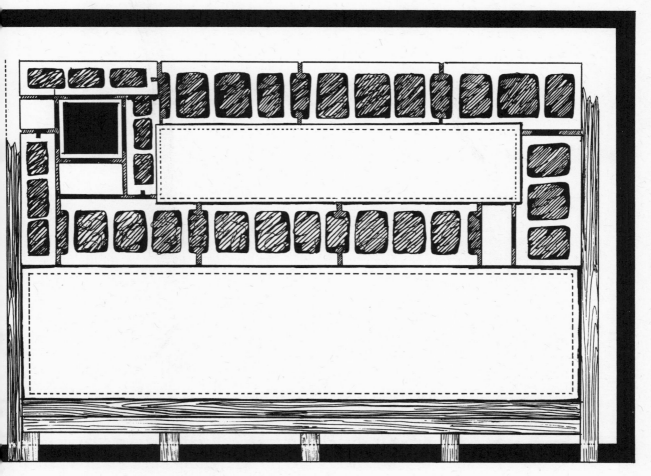

5-2. Top view of foundation with holes filled.

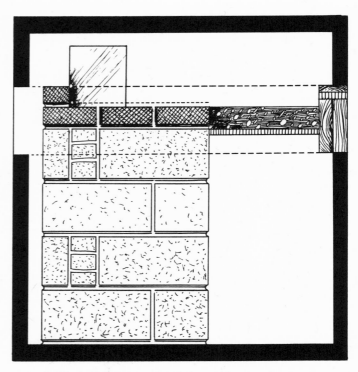

5-3. Subhearth is poured; brickwork begins for breast.

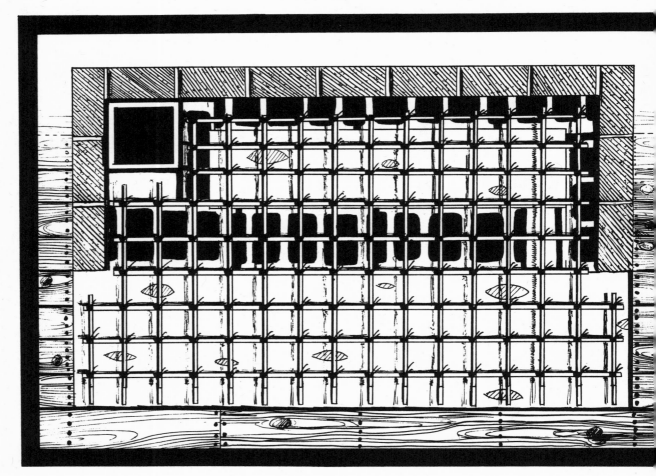

5-4. Reinforcing rod in place, ready to pour subhearth.

The Firebox

We are now ready to begin brick work for the jambs and breast, continue the inside chimney for the basement flue, and start on the firebox.

Firebox Opening-Jambs

For the time being, leave the front hearth empty. There's no sense in laying bricks there now since they'd only get messed up during the rest of the building. However, for the back hearth (the floor of the firebox), lay bricks in a pattern that will match that of the front hearth. Extend the pattern far enough back and to the sides to allow the firebox bricks to sit entirely on top of the hearth bricks. (See Figure 5-5)

5-5. Extend brickwork pattern far enough back and to the sides of the back hearth.

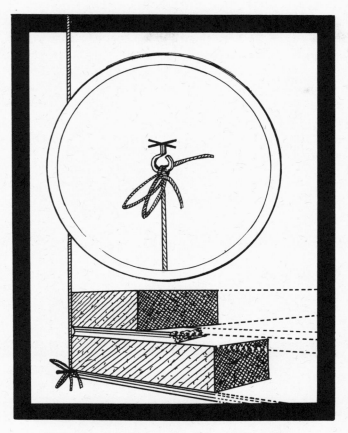

5–6. Plumb lines help the job considerably.

Generally, I find it easier to begin this phase of the fireplace by bringing up the jambs and breast first. Drop plumb lines from the ceiling (Figure 5-6) or from the corners of the ceiling cut out if you're that far ahead.

After completing your block work, I'm sure you've noticed two things immediately about working with brick. First, each unit is much lighter and considerably easier to handle and second, progress is much slower than when laying block.

Set your brick leads the same as your block: plumb, level, and square. A ⅜-inch joint is standard for most brick work. The thinner a joint, the nicer it will look. If you're using old bricks which vary in size, be wary of trying to execute too thin a joint.

Set the brick with one hand, one end buttered, down into the mortar (Figure 5-7). Then level it to the line with a tap or two with the trowel blade or trowel handle (Figure 5-8). As with blocks, check the level line to be sure no pieces of mortar are pushing it out of true. One piece of advice here for setting leads with brick: After you set a lead brick to the plumb line and you're ready to set a brick next to it, don't butter the end of the next brick. The buttered brick will have a tendency to push the lead brick out of place. Set your next brick, then fill the joint from above (Figure 5-9).

To bring up the jambs, a 2-foot level will be adequate to keep them plumb, but always check the plane of the face by using line blocks (large plate) or by using a long straight-edge. It's easy to keep the bricks plumb and level but lose sight of the overall face.

Bring the breast and jambs up and around for seven or eight courses. Then we'll be ready to start the firebox and build the arch.

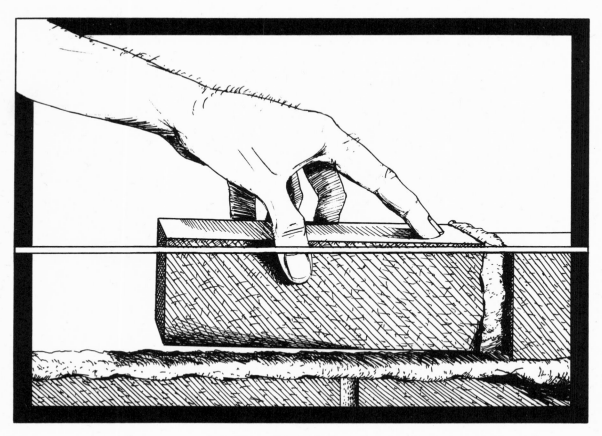

5–7. You will have to learn how best to keep your thumb from disturbing the line.

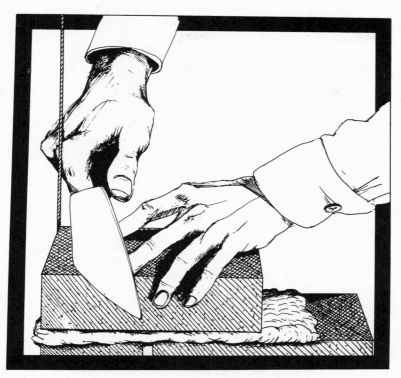

5-8. A few taps of the trowel will level the lead brick.

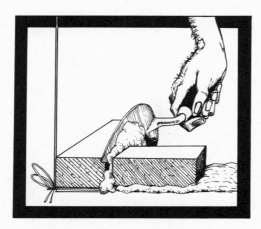

5-9. Fill the joint next to a lead brick after the brick has been laid.

The Rumford Firebox

As I suggested earlier, any extensive Rumford investigation is left to you. I feel my role in spreading his gospel is more nuts and bolts than history and physics.

Before we actually lay out and build a Rumford firebox, then, there are several points you should know. First, Rumford's principles are not as strict as most people think. The depth of the firebox, which is the outstanding feature, can, by Rumford's standards, be anywhere from one-third to one-half the dimension of the opening.

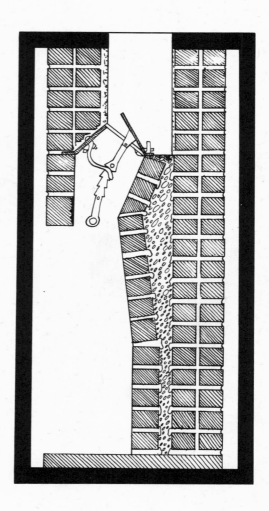

As you can see, that permits two quite different fireboxes to choose from. I prefer the more shallow firebox as it is much more graceful and tends to throw more heat.

Rumford also decided that the firebox opening should be as high as it is wide. For some reason, when a firebox is exactly as high as it is wide it *looks taller*. The shallow depth of the firebox and the gentle slope of the back wall add to this illusion of height and grace.

The firebox illustrated here takes a little from each of Rumford's possible designs. It is 32 inches wide since that's what remains after deciding on a two-brick jamb on each side (with 64 inches overall). It is 12 inches deep because (1) it is extremely close to 1/3 of the opening and (2) by going back 12 inches (into a 16-inch-wide back) the side walls of the firebox, or covings, become 12 inches. (Even brick cuts are pleasing to the eye.)

The type of brick you use in the firebox is up to you. It is not necessary to use firebrick, although there is nothing wrong with it. I recommend a smooth-faced, regular hard brick set in the same mortar that is used for the rest of the fireplace. Most books recommend a fireclay or fire mortar for the firebox. Frankly, I have never used it nor do I know anyone who has used anything but regular mortar for a firebox.

Cutting and shaping the bricks for the firebox is not difficult, but it can be frustrating. (See Figures 5-10, 5-11, and 5-12) Use a brick set if you like, or shape the bricks entirely with your brick hammer. There will be times when a particular brick simply will not comply. Don't despair—pick up another and try again. You'll find that your discarded bricks will not be wasted. Even if they're used only for fill, there is a place for them.

5–10, 5–11. Be patient when
cutting bricks. It may take some
practice to get comfortable with it.

5–12. Bricks may not always break where you want them to.

Laying Brick for the Firebox

The back wall of the firebox should be vertical for about 14 or 15 inches (wherever there is an even course). It should then slope inward at an angle such that it will end at a width of about 6 inches and at a height of 6 inches or so above the opening of the firebox. (The damper door gives us Rumford's 4-inch throat opening.)

If you're using a standard damper, the covings and back wall will flare back from this point to meet the damper. (More on this later.) If you're going to custom-make a damper, extend the plane of your back wall to a point about 9 inches above the opening and 4 inches from the brick work above the arch.

Lay out a side view of your firebox to determine the degree of angle to use. This is not terribly difficult. The best way to do it is to draw it out, full size, on cardboard or paper, or even on the floor or wall. The important thing here is to line up the center of your firebox as closely as possible with the center of the throat.

This may not work out as nicely as all the Rumford firebox line drawings you've probably seen, and there are good reasons why. The main reason is that since everyone's home and framing is different, it is difficult to apply such definitive, straightforward principles to a dozen different alternatives. Just keep in mind Rumford's main principles—heat goes out in a straight line from its source, and smoke *wants* to go up; hence let it.

I've found that the best way to maintain the proper angle of the fireback as you're actually laying up bricks is to set your bevel at the angle needed, tighten it securely, then mark and cut each coving brick as you need it (Figure 5-13). As the back slopes inward the coving courses will shorten. Remember to keep your bonding consistent with the lower courses, even if it means a particularly small cut. The overall effect of even bonding is essential.

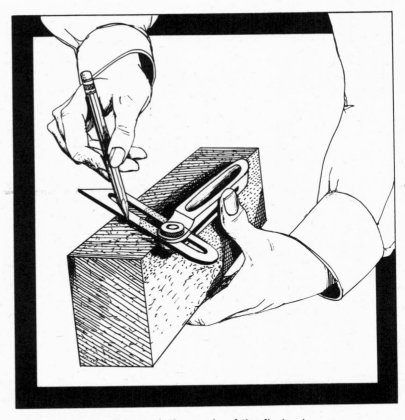

5–13. Use a bevel to mark the angle of the fireback.

5-14. You may want to stiffen up the mortar for the slope bricks.

Keep the firebox bricks on even courses with the breast; this ends up looking much nicer than if you don't. I generally start by laying up two or three courses of the back wall first. The width of the fireback will want to overlap the covings a bit, so set up the back and then set the covings *to* it. I also find it helps to mark a plumb line on the back bricks before setting covings to it.

The slope of the fireback might be a bit difficult for you because the bricks have a tendency to slip forward. The best way to solve this problem is to stiffen up your mortar enough to prevent the bricks from slipping. It may take a little practice getting the slope bricks to sit properly, but they will (Figure 5-14).

Since the three sides of the firebox are not tied into each other, you will find that after you get up a few courses the bricks may have a tendency to wobble. This is expected and normal; just be a little more gentle and a bit more patient. Keep filling in with rubble behind the back and covings as you go. Building a firebox is fairly cramped and exacting work. Get as comfortable as you can—a rubber pad for your knees and your favorite music in the background help.

As far as procedure is concerned, generally build up the jambs to the height of the lintel, or in this case, the point at which the arch begins (see "The Arch" below). Then build up the firebox to the same height. Next, build the arch and tie in the face to a height of two courses above the arch (which will be the height to install the damper). Then go back and finish the firebox. (If you prefer a square or rectangular opening for your firebox, simply install a steel angle iron (lintel) at the desired height and run your courses across it. Damper installation remains the same.)

The Arch

Since the jambs, firebox, and arch are all being built simultaneously, you should have your arch form built and ready to use ahead of time. An arch adds an extra dimension of grace to a predominantly rectangular structure. Since arches are extremely simple to build I find it odd that there aren't more of them.

For the arch you first need to build a form for the arch bricks to sit on. Use two pieces of ¾-inch stock (plywood is fine) sandwiched around two pieces of 2-by-3-inch stock. The resulting width will be about 4 inches (depending on where you get your lumber). The length of the form will equal the firebox opening, and the degree of curve will depend on you. (See Figure 5-15)

Regardless of the degree of curve you give the arch, keep two things in mind. First, the top of the form (bottom of arch bricks) should be as high as the fireplace is wide. If your brick courses prevent this, don't worry. Get as close as possible without being *under*. In fact, two or three inches higher than the width looks great and works perfectly. Second, lay out the curve in such a way that the *top* of the arch bricks come out at an even course of bricks. This will eliminate an unsightly brick cut at the top of the arch. You can do this by measuring or by laying bricks out on the floor.

Install the form any way you wish but remember it has to come out soon. I support it on 2-by-4s with wedges under them. When removing the form, first pull the wedges. The form will drop straight down and out without disturbing the arch bricks. Make sure the arch form is sturdy and secure before you lay the arch bricks. Arch bricks are merely half bricks laid on edge. Lay the rectangular edges to the curved arch, starting from either side and working toward the middle. The resulting joints will be wedge-shaped. Keep the bottom of the wedge joint the same thickness as the vertical joints in the rest of the fireplace.

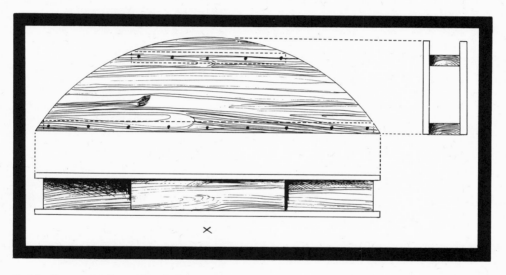

5–15. Cross section of arch form.

5–16. Arch form in place with first course of bricks. Keep your bonding consistent.

After laying the arch bricks, fill in a course or two above the arch. Here you will be far enough along to remove the arch form. If you can remove the form before the mortar is set completely, you will be able to tool the joints on the underside of the arch with ease. If you don't think you'll be able to finish in time, leave out ½ inch of mortar in the bottom of the arch joints and fill the next day. This is painstaking but worth it for appearance (Figure 5-16).

The first time I built an arch I was so afraid it wouldn't work that I wouldn't remove the form for two days. Sure enough, it did not fall down and I spent several hours chiseling out the messy joints and repointing them.

The most difficult job of brick cutting that you will have will involve the bricks that run into the arch. The cutting principles involved are the same as straight cuts, but curves require more patience. Scribe the curve you need on the brick and work your cut from both sides. You may destroy several bricks before you get your cut just right. This is perfectly normal so don't worry.

CHAPTER 6:

SMOKE SHELF AND SMOKE CHAMBER

Your firebox is complete and your damper about to be installed. Now it's time to begin the much touted smoke chamber and take a look at the even more touted smoke shelf.

The Smoke Shelf

I won't belabor the point, but it is virtually impossible to build a masonry firebox (Rumford or not) without having the smoke shelf appear *all by itself* as a natural extension of the fireback. I consider its function as "bouncer of cold air back up the chimney" ridiculous. I never once knew a gust of cold air polite enough to follow the arrows, stay on the back side of the flue and smoke chamber, and wait its turn to be firmly rebuked by the strong, silent, and "absolutely essential" smoke shelf. The smoke shelf is there because it is the *top* of the sloped fireback and the *bottom* of the smoke chamber which must be considerably wider than the 4-inch opening for the throat.

The Smoke Chamber

The smoke chamber also has to be there, but it does serve a very useful function. Basically, it is a funnel for the hot air and unburned gasses (smoke). The more height and less acute angle you can give your smoke chamber, the better chance smoke will have to rise. (Try this experiment in your kitchen as an example in reverse: find two funnels, one shallow and one more elongated. Pour a cup of water in each. See which drains faster and easier.)

The first task in preparing the smoke chamber is to install the damper. Using a standard damper for your Rumford firebox may frustrate you. Your plumb lines and center lines just don't conform to all you've learned about Rumford's principles. It's very easy to present line drawings with obedient arrows and to trust proven mathematical formulas yet quite another to execute them.

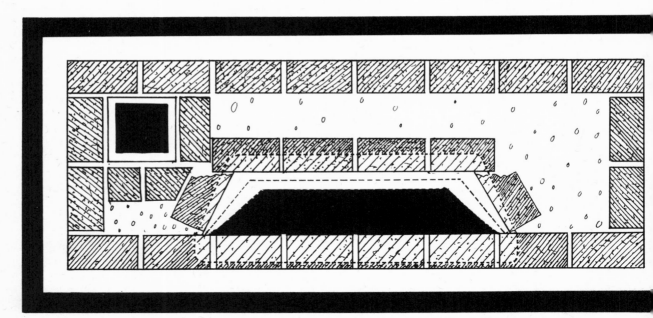

6–1. Dotted lines indicate position of damper on adjusted fireback.

A standard 33-inch cast-iron poker damper will not sit comfortably on top of your Rumford firebox. But you do have two alternatives and they both work beautifully. You could have a damper custom-made to your specifications using ⅜- or ¼-inch steel. This would incorporate the same design as a stock damper except the angle from front to back would be sharper to match your covings. I have done this. It's time-consuming, expensive, and makes absolutely no difference in the proper functioning of a Rumford firebox.

The other option is to use a standard damper. To do this, install it on the second course above the arch, and flare back the last three courses of fireback and covings to meet the sides and back of the damper. (See Figure 6-1) You will notice that this adjustment takes place above the opening of the firebox and in no way affects the heat-throwing properties of the firebox, its visual properties, or the draft of smoke that goes into the smoke chamber. It is true that if you need to step back your chimney to go up the outside of your house, you will not be able to line up the center of your back hearth with the front third of your fireplace flue, as Rumford suggests. You will be able to follow Rumford's smoke chamber and flue dimensions more closely if you keep the chimney breast inside the house, but you will still be forced to custom-make a damper or flare back the fireback to accommodate a standard one. This is fine—adjust your layout by a brick thickness (enough to allow for a full brick thickness plus a flue liner next to any house framing.)

With the damper set in place, the smoke chamber will begin to take shape (Figure 6-2). The damper will be set on top of the covings and fireback. Since the covings and the fireback may not end up exactly on the same level (because of the fireback slope), set the damper in a bed of mortar thick enough to allow for the discrepancy.

The back and front walls are vertical and the side walls slope at a gradual angle to meet at the opening of the flue liner at a height of about 4 feet above the throat. The back wall of the smoke chamber will start approximately 4 inches behind the damper door, at the level of the base of the damper. This wall will be the thickness of a brick. At a point about 16 to 18 inches below the flue, you should begin to slope the back wall so that it will meet the 12-inch base of the flue tile. Have the last course of the front wall create about a 1-inch ledge so the tile will have bearing on all four sides. (See Figure 6-3)

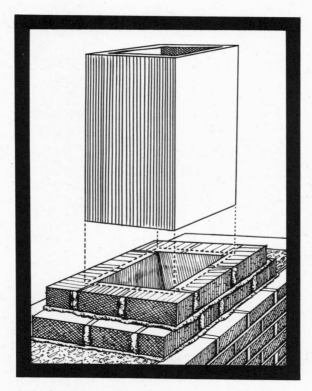

6-3. Smoke chamber creates bearing for flue tile.

Opposite page:

6-2. Top: damper and smoke chamber detail. Bottom: damper installed on fireback.

In some places you may see the smoke chamber done without a double wall to the outside. I prefer this double wall for two reasons: to insulate against the cold and to create a tighter funnel effect in the smoke chamber. The less "dead air" space you have the faster the smoke will rise.

As you can see in the cutout section illustrated in Figure 8-1, the double wall on the inside is there because of the eventual step-in of the breast if you're going up the outside. If you're not, try using the step-in at mantel height. (See Figure 6-4) This creates a convenient platform for the mantelpiece to sit on. (See Figures 6-5 and 6-6)

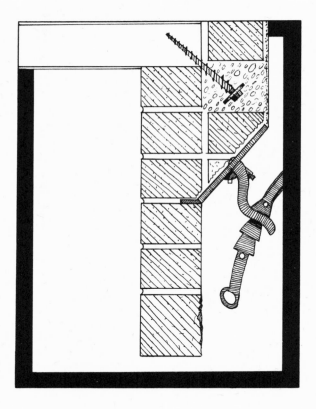

6–4, 6–5, 6–6. Various ways to install a mantelpiece.

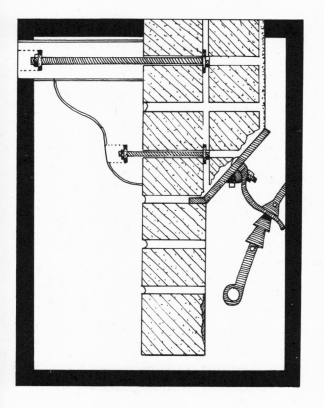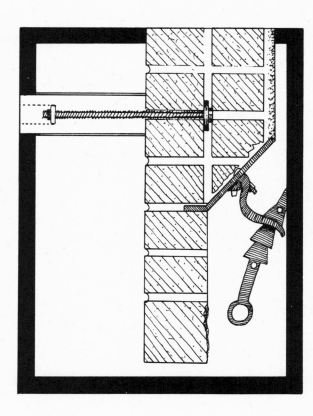

If you've done your homework and looked up and into a number of smoke chambers, you will have noticed that few, if any, are smoothed off. If you smooth off the inside of a smoke chamber with mortar, it will (1) let the smoke escape faster, (2) be *so* much easier to clean as years go by, and (3) give you the satisfaction of helping Count Rumford rest easier in his grave! (See Figure 6-7)

As you come up with the smoke chamber you will realize that there is a considerable amount to do inside the breast that will never be visible. You must continue the basement flue tile and the bricks that enclose it. And you must also fill any gaps on the front side of the basement flue. The right side of the smoke chamber must also be filled. Rubble and scrap are fine here, but I think you'll find concrete blocks fill things up faster. Remember, you don't have to be neat here but you must be solid.

With regard to procedure, it probably makes more sense to bring everything up at once. Come up with three or four courses of the smoke chamber, smoothing the inside as you go. Then fill both sides and run a few courses of the face. You'll be up on your staging now so materials won't be as easy to handle. This is another phase of the construction where it's a good idea to relax and concentrate on being steady instead of fast.

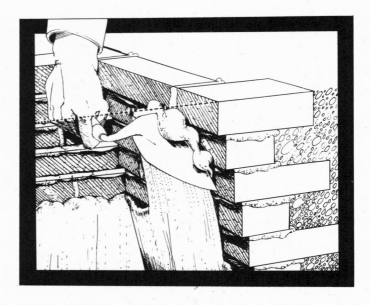

6-7. Smooth off the inside of the smoke chamber as you go.

CHAPTER 7:

CHIMNEY

After the smoke chamber is complete, install the first fireplace flue tile. From this point on we must step the basement and fireplace flue tiles together to create a compact chimney. This can be done in one of two ways: step the fireplace flue tile to join the basement flue tile or step the basement flue tile to join the fireplace flue tile. Either way is correct, but generally the neater and less complicated way is easier and better.

If this is done outside the house, you will need to present a water-repellent surface. Create the sloped surface with bricks or a stone such as bluestone (Figures 7-1, 7-2). If you're staying inside the house, step in any way you wish.

When bringing together the flue tiles, remember that the empty spaces will have to be filled. There is still a great deal of weight in the rest of the chimney which must be supported. For fill, use any kind of masonry: brick, block, or scrap. Again, solid bearing is necessary.

When cutting tiles for the step-in of the chimney, keep in mind that you will have to make your cuts in such a way that the tiles fit together properly. So, when you know where your angle is going, and what angle it will be (no greater than 30 degrees), *think ahead* and cut the top of your last vertical tile to match the bottom of the angled tile. At this point it might not be a bad idea to lay out the tiles on the floor, calculate your angles, and cut them ahead of time. The less you go back and forth to your staging, the smoother the job will go.

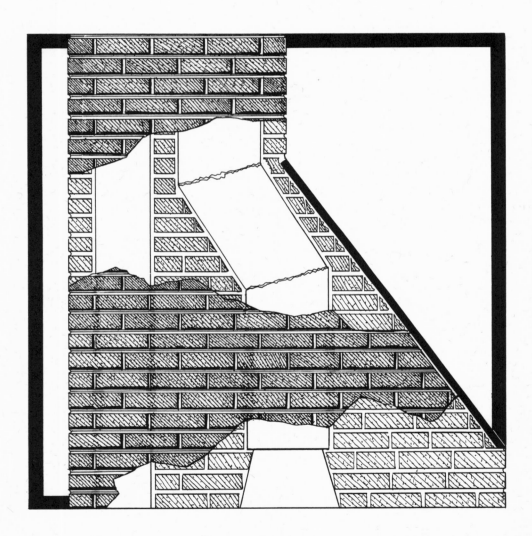

7–1, 7–2. Outside cross section of chimney. Stone or slate will act as water shedder.

As you build the chimney, a certain amount of mortar will fall down the flue tile. To prevent a *solid* mess, stuff something like a burlap bag into the smoke chamber to keep the smoke shelf and damper clean.

Plumb lines will help you immeasurably with your chimney. If you're building inside, drop them from the ceiling or from the roof rafters. (Remember the 2-inch firestop.)

If you're building outside, make a jig to fasten to the exposed sheathing or perhaps to the roof. Sometimes it's a pain to take the time for setting up plumb lines, but it will save you a lot of time in the long run.

Staging

Inside construction will require very little staging. Good solid saw horses with 2-inch-thick planks suffice nicely. Outside, however, staging is critical and safety, essential. Your best bet is to rent good solid pipe staging. Be sure the staging is set level and is erected plumb. Its four legs should be set with pads on solid ground. I've heard stories of staging loaded with bricks tipping over during a heavy rain because the legs sank into the ground. (See Figure 7-3)

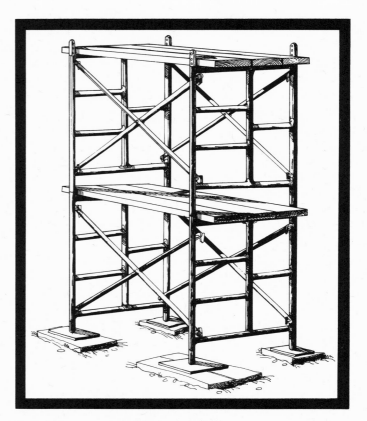

7–3. Use a good, solid pipe staging.

Flashing

Flashing is an element of the chimney experience that most people find mysterious and difficult. It can be both. Frankly, if you've never installed flashing before, I'd advise you to seek some personal instruction.

Flashing drawings (including mine) are very neat and orderly. They relate to an ideal situation because we can't use up the space required for all the possible combinations of flashing details. You cannot afford to make a mistake in your flashing; otherwise your roof will leak. I will explain the principles, but if you still have any questions, get them answered.

When a chimney interrupts the siding or roofing of a house, it must somehow restore the water-shedding properties it has interrupted. Flashing will fold itself from the bricks of the chimney into the siding or roofing material in such a way that it sheds water. I suggest you use lead or copper flashing. It comes in rolls of almost any width you would need. Lead and copper are quite expensive but well worth their cost for durability, workability, and appearance.

Side flashing is quite simple. As you go up the outside of the house, fold a precut piece of flashing onto the brick and straight up the side of the sheathing. (See Figure 7-4) Do this every two courses, keeping the flashing neat and straight. Be sure the pieces overlap each other by at least 2 inches.

Flashing for the brick work around the roof line is more complicated and can vary quite a bit depending on the size of the chimney, pitch of the roof, and so forth.

If your chimney comes up through the eave or roof, you may need more than flashing to shed water or prevent a buildup of snow and ice. A separate structure, built onto the roof and butting into the chimney will serve to shed water. This is commonly called a "cricket" (Figure 7-5). The flashing details for the cricket would be the same as in Figure 7-6. In essence, you're building a small roof with one specific purpose. As with the side flashing, roof and cricket flashing will fold itself from the bricks into the roofing material. Be sure to overlap the shingles and flashing to keep a water-repellent surface. *Do not* nail the flashing and *do not* use roofing tar of any sort.

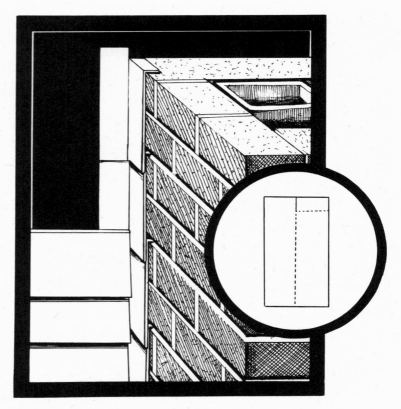

7-4. Fold flashing into the bricks and up the side of the house.

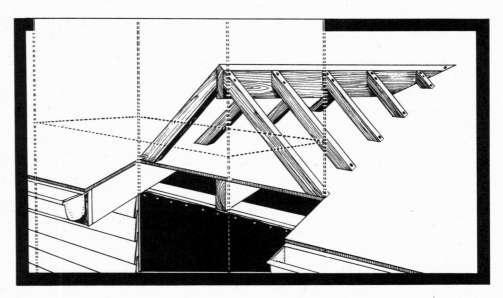

7-5. Treat your cricket as a small roof. Shingle and flash likewise.

7–6. Peak flashing, gable end.

Most local building codes recommend that a chimney extend at least 2 feet above the peak of the roof. Generally, this is a good rule of thumb but be sure to check out your local conditions. Often a higher chimney will help the draft if your house is in a low pressure area (valley, or foot of a hill). If time is on your side, have your first fire before you remove your chimney staging.

There are many interesting ways to finish the chimney and hundreds of variations on the theme of shedding water. With your new awareness, you'll begin to notice an amazing variety of chimney tops.

The last few feet of your chimney are quite important. Again, check local codes to find out if your chimney needs to be thicker above the roof line. This is sometimes the case.

Figure 7-7 shows the most basic way to end a chimney. Just stop laying bricks about 8 or 10 inches below the top of the flue tile. Lay mortar on the bricks and between the tiles so that it fills all cracks, and smooth it off so it can shed water. It's also a good idea to end the flue tiles at different levels. This helps prevent downdraft from one flue to another.

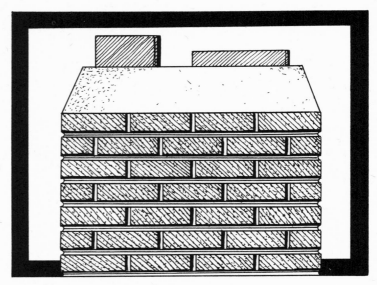

7-7. Simple way to end a chimney.

Figure 7-8 shows a typical "cap" which will eliminate a considerable amount of wind and weather from going down the flue. There are many different caps and they all attack a different problem; so think about this before you remove your staging.

Finally, Figure 7-9 shows one possible way to add weight to the chimney in an attractive way.

I would only add one more thing here about bricks. You will probably want to wash your bricks when you finish the job. No matter how neat you've been, there will be smudges of mortar and mortar dust on the bricks. Muriatic acid is the commercial name for an acid that eats cement. Most masonry supply yards, lumber yards, and hardware stores carry the acid. Dilute it with water (follow directions on label) and scrub. Rubber gloves, goggles, and a long-handled brush are a good idea.

7–8. Chimney with a stone cap.

7–9. Extra width gives added weight to the chimney.

CHAPTER 8:

CONCLUSION

There's not much more to discuss except that as you build your fireplace you'll learn for yourself more than I can possibly convey to you. The guidelines I've presented will be very useful and your own interest and hard work will make up for the rest.

There are, however, a few points I'd like to mention. Some will serve simply as reminders; others as new information.

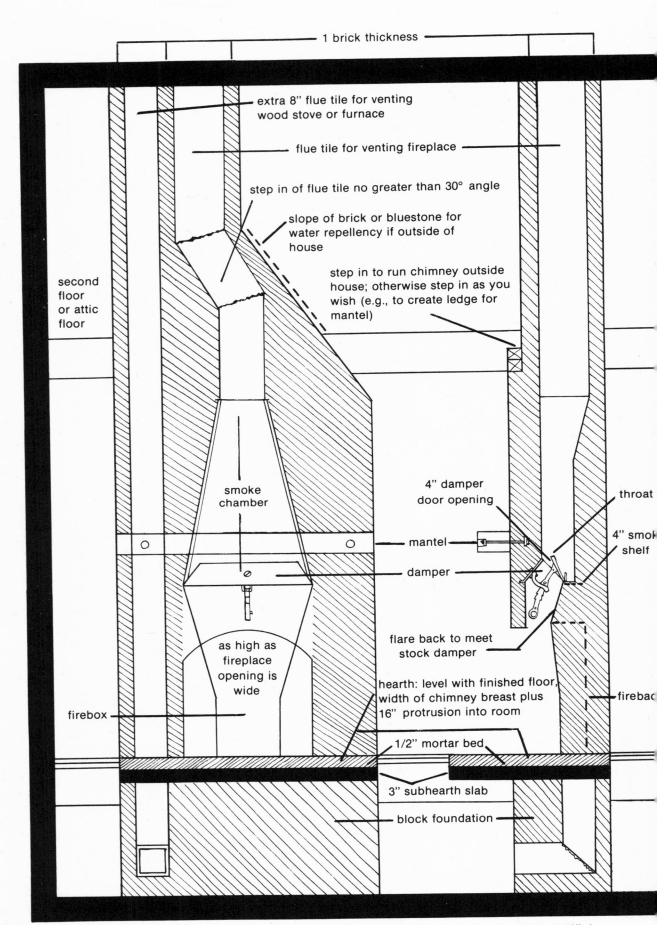

1 brick thickness

extra 8" flue tile for venting wood stove or furnace

flue tile for venting fireplace

step in of flue tile no greater than 30° angle

slope of brick or bluestone for water repellency if outside of house

step in to run chimney outside house; otherwise step in as you wish (e.g., to create ledge for mantel)

second floor or attic floor

smoke chamber

4" damper door opening

throat

4" smoke shelf

mantel

damper

flare back to meet stock damper

fireback

as high as fireplace opening is wide

hearth: level with finished floor, width of chimney breast plus 16" protrusion into room

firebox

1/2" mortar bed

3" subhearth slab

block foundation

footing: level with house footing; 8" wider than chimney breast and 12" deep

Before you start:

1. If you're not knowledgeable in house construction, check with someone who is and figure the best location for the fireplace. Take your time with this initial consideration and get a picture of what will go where. (See Figures 8-1 and 8-2)

2. Safety codes vary so be sure to double check. Your layout will have to correspond with local safety standards, so take whatever time is necessary to plan the actual structure before you build. Know your local building codes, and obtain a permit if necessary.

3. The size of your flue will depend on the opening of your firebox (or vice versa). The area of the flue should be 1/10 the area of the firebox opening. Be sure the flue size you need is a standard one. If not, play it safe and use one size larger.

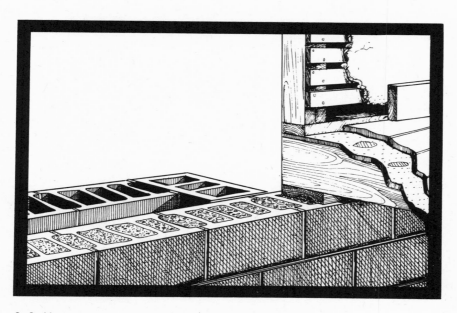

8-2. You may have to cut a hole in your living room wall.

Opposite page:

8-1. Overall cross section: know where your structure will take you.

4. Most codes call for a firestop of some sort where the chimney passes through framing but not when the chimney goes up the outside of the house. A firestop code generally calls for a 2-inch space between the chimney and the framing which is filled with a non-combustible material. This is a fairly obscure code. It is mentioned everywhere but rarely executed. Please investigate this particular code. There is usually a good reason for such codes.

5. Chimney codes require the use of a flue liner for each thing (furnace, water heater, wood stove, fireplace) to be vented. Each liner should be separated from another liner by 3½ inches (a brick thickness).

6. Chimney thicknesses vary. A brick chimney will require a brick thickness plus the flue liner. A block chimney will require 8 inches plus the flue liner. A stone chimney usually requires 10 to 12 inches plus a flue liner. Depending on local conditions, some areas require that chimneys expand in thickness (hence weight) above the roof line. This added weight will insure stability against heavy winds.

As I said at the start of this book, there is plenty of hard work in building your own fireplace; but the end result is well worth it. I'm including here a letter I received from friends who built their own fireplace. They consulted me numerous times and in fact built their fireplace as I wrote this book. Their enthusiasm for the finished product is obvious.

Hi Zack—
As I'm writing this, there's a fire going in our Rumford fireplace. Outside there's a storm from the southeast and heavy rain, but inside it's a different world with a quiet fire going.
The job has surpassed our greatest hopes! The fireplace draws beautifully in all wind directions and conditions so far.
Anyway, we think of you often and will always remember your great advice and the confidence you gave us to complete this project ourselves. You have a standing invite to come see us any time.
Our best,
Dave and Linda

GLOSSARY

Back Hearth—Floor of the firebox, rear section of the hearth.

"Bats"—Sections of brick, usually ½ to ¾ original length.

Bond—The pattern created when courses of bricks are laid.

Breast—Chimney breast. A fairly loose term indicating the main face of the chimney.

"Butter"—A term used to describe the application of mortar to the ends of brick or block.

Cap—Chimney cap. Extension on top of the chimney to prevent down drafts, arrest sparks, and shed water. Often quite ornate and lovely. (Keep your eyes open.)

Corbel—A structural unit that projects outward and upward from the vertical. The act of placing that unit.

Covings—Side walls of the firebox.

Cricket—A structure built between the roof and chimney to shed water and snow.

Damper—A metal, dome-shaped contraption with a hinged door. The damper sits on top of the firebox and its "door" helps control the draft into the smoke chamber.

"Dressed"—Stone that has been cut and trimmed to a specific dimension and then generally smoothed.

"Ears"—The protruding ends of a concrete block.

Fireback—The back wall of the firebox.

Firebox—The place where the fire burns.

Firestop—A space between the wood framing of a house and the chimney, usually filled with a noncombustible material to keep the fire from spreading.

Flange—A rim around or on something to provide strength or provide surface for an attachment.

Flashing—Sheet metal, bent and folded from the chimney into the roof or side of a house to shed water.

Flue—The space inside the chimney that lets the hot air and gasses escape.

Flue Tile or **Flue Liner**—A ceramic pipe (rectangular or circular) that lines the flue passage.

Footing—Solid concrete base of the chimney that is always below the frost line.

Front Hearth—The portion of the fireplace that extends into the room.

Header—A construction term referring to a framing member that spans other framing members to "head them off" when a hole in the framing is required.

Hearth—The floor of the fireplace, front and back.

Jambs—Uprights on either side of the firebox.

Jointer—A jointing tool used to smooth and harden masonry joints.

Joist—A horizontal framing member.

Lead—As in "follow the leader," a term used to describe the masonry units set first.

Line Blocks—Plastic or wooden gadgets to which you attach a string to stretch between leads to create a level course.

Lintel—A structural member (usually steel) that bridges the top of the fireplace supporting the masonry.

Mantel—Mantel is a fairly loose term. It is used to describe the entire finished structure around the fireplace. If there is only a shelf above the fireplace, it is referred to as a "mantel" or "mantelpiece." The arch or lintel that supports the masonry above the firebox jambs is also referred to as the mantel.

Plumb—Exactly vertical.

Quarry Rubble—Pieces of stone "left over" after excavation, cutting, and dressing.

Reinforcing Rod—Lengths of round steel bar set in concrete for added strength.

Smoke Chamber—The area between the damper and the flue system, a funnel of sorts to help smoke escape.

Smoke Shelf—The area behind the damper, at the base of the smoke chamber, which is created by the fireback. Some attribute "magical" properties to the smoke shelf.

Staging (Scaffolding)—Steel or wooden erection that supports people and building materials while work is being done above ground.

Strike—To scrape mortar from joints with the trowel.

Subfloor—Lumber nailed to floor joists upon which the finished floor will sit.

Subhearth—Concrete slab used as a base for the finished hearth.

Throat—The opening at the top of the firebox that allows smoke to enter the smoke chamber.

"Tool"—To finish masonry joints with a jointing tool.

Yard—A measure of volume equal to 27 cubic feet.

ANNOTATED BIBLIOGRAPHY

Brann, Donald R. *How to Install a Fireplace*. Briar Cliff Manor, New York: Directions Simplified, Inc., 1974.

Daniels, M.E. *Fireplaces and Wood Stoves: How to Build, Buy, Install and Use Them*. New York: Bobbs-Merrill, 1977.

Eastman, Wilbur, and Eastman, Margaret. *Planning and Building Your Fireplace*. Charlotte, New Hampshire: Garden Way Publishing, 1976.

Editors of Sunset Books. *How to Plan and Build Fireplaces*. Menlo Park, California: Lane Books, 1974.

Gay, Larry. *The Complete Book of Heating with Wood*. Charlotte, New Hampshire: Garden Way Publishing, 1976. This book covers all aspects of heating with wood. It is aimed mainly at wood stoves; however, it gives abundant information on burning properties of wood. Highly recommended.

Kern, Ken; Magers, Steve; and Penfield, Lou. *Stone Masonry*. Oakhurst, California: Owner Built Publications, 1976.

Lytle, R. J., and Lytle, Marie-Jeanne. *Book of Successful Fireplaces*. Farmington, Michigan: Structures Publishing Co., 1971.

Orton, Vrest. *The Forgotten Art of Building a Good Fireplace*. Dublin, New Hampshire: Yankee Inc., 1974. An absolute must.

Rowsome, Frank Jr. *The Bright and Glowing Place*. Brattleboro, Vermont: Stephen Green Press, 1975. Nice book in the fireside, storytelling tradition.

Rumford, Count. *Collected Works*. Edited by Sanborn C. Brown. Cambridge, Massachusetts: Harvard University Press, 1976.

INDEX

Much thought, effort and expense have gone into the writing, publishing and preparing of this book. Return it to your library on time and in good condition so that others may enjoy it. If you wish to add a copy to your personal library, it probably is available at your local bookstore.

**YOUR
SALT LAKE CITY
PUBLIC LIBRARY**

DEMCO